How to Relax

How to Relax

How to Relax

Enhancing your Mental and Physical Health through the Art of Inner Self-Regulation

Patrick Davis, Ph.D.

Writers Club Press
San Jose New York Lincoln Shanghai

How to Relax
Enhancing your Mental and Physical Health through
the Art of Inner Self-Regulation

Writers Club Press
an imprint of iUniverse.com, Inc.

For information address:
iUniverse.com, Inc.
5220 S 16th, Ste. 200
Lincoln, NE 68512
www.iuniverse.com

ISBN: 0-595-17441-8

Printed in the United States of America

ACKNOWLEDGMENTS

George Rice first introduced me to the idea of relaxation training many years ago when I was an undergraduate at Montana State University. Fred Heide brought an academic and clinical interest in relaxation training back into my life during my years as a graduate student at the California School of Professional Psychology. Over the past few years, as I have been learning more about the practice and uses of relaxation, the clients in my private practice of psychotherapy have taught me much about the successful application of relaxation to real life problems.

My understanding and practice of relaxation has been influenced tremendously by the work of Herbert Benson, M.D., Jonathan Smith, Ph.D., and Jon Kabat-Zinn, Ph.D.

I particularly wish to thank Gina Hartung, Tom Kinney, Melanie Lattin, Mona Morstein, and Bob Unterseher for their generous assistance with the seemingly endless task of reviewing and editing the manuscript once the initial writing phase of the project was completed.

CONTENTS

INTRODUCTION

I have written this book to assist people who want to learn to be more relaxed so that they may enjoy a greater level of physical and emotional well being. As a practicing clinical psychologist, I frequently provide my clients with instruction in relaxation to help them learn to more effectively manage a wide range of emotional, behavioral, interpersonal, and physical problems. Over the years I have purchased, read, and recommended a wide variety of the books and audio-cassette tapes on the topic of relaxation; however, I have never been able to find a resource for my clients which has truly met their needs in an optimal manner. While many books on the topic of relaxation are available, a number of problems with these materials repeatedly seem to crop up. Some books are too long and detailed to hold the interest of many readers and so are set aside before any significant learning occurs. Others focus exclusively on one problem area and as such are not general enough to meet the needs of a wide range of readers. Some include one or more chapters on relaxation but then cover an overly broad canvas with the result that they overwhelm the reader with too much information. Some are not sensitive to the religious or spiritual concerns of readers and so are discarded because they are viewed as challenging or threatening to the reader's religious beliefs. It has been my intent to overcome these problems with this book.

The book is brief and to the point so that readers will be able to read the entire text in one or two sittings. It is general enough to meet the needs of anyone who wishes to learn to relax for any reason while at the same time being comprehensive in its coverage of the topic. The entire focus of the book is on how to learn to relax one's mind and body deeply and rapidly. As a result, readers will not be distracted from this focus or discouraged by having to wade through unnecessary material unrelated to this one important topic. Finally, I have made an effort to be sensitive to the differing religious or spiritual perspectives of the wide audience the book is written for. The sections on mental imagery and meditation are written in a clearly secular manner although the reader certainly may incorporate aspects of his or her religious or spiritual orientation into these relaxation approaches. I have included a section on prayer as an approach to relaxation in an effort to make the book and the practice of relaxation more accessible to the large numbers of readers who wish to pursue wellness in a manner that clearly embraces their religious beliefs.

In addition to attempting to overcome these problems, this book also describes relatively recent advances in our understanding of how one moves through the process of first learning to practice relaxation for twenty or thirty minutes on a daily basis to developing the ability to relax rapidly even in very stressful situations.

As a practicing psychotherapist, I have repeatedly worked with clients who have developed the ability to relax reasonably deeply with the assistance of audio-cassette relaxation tapes or biofeedback. Many of those same clients, however, never successfully move beyond these learning tools to develop the ability to relax rapidly in stressful situations without having to retreat to their bedroom to listen to a tape or to their therapist's office for a booster biofeedback session. I have attempted to overcome this barrier to effective application of relaxation by emphasizing the importance of, and by describing a method for, working toward independence from relaxation tapes.

It is my sincere belief that anyone who is troubled by excessive stress, behavioral or interpersonal problems, or stress related physical ailments will derive significant benefit from learning the skill of relaxation. It is my genuine desire that this book finds its way into the hands of those individuals who not only understand that they would benefit from learning the skill of relaxation, but who also believe that through their own efforts at self-regulation they can come to enjoy enhanced physical and emotional well being.

One

Prelude

A CARROT

Begin by taking a slow, smooth, deep breath. Try to breath from your abdomen and not from your chest. Take a few more of these deep breaths. As you exhale, repeat the word "relax" silently to yourself. With each outward breath, as you silently repeat the word "relax," imagine all of the muscles in your body loosening up. Now, count backward from ten to one while you take ten more deep, relaxing breaths. Do this now, before you turn the page. With each breath let all of the muscles in your body become more and more relaxed.

Why You should Learn to Relax

"All the evils of the world are due to the fact that
man cannot sit still in a room."
—Jean Cocteau

The value of developing and using the skill of relaxation for the cultivation and maintenance of physical and emotional health has gained tremendous recognition in recent years. We now know that the benefits of relaxation extend beyond being a useful tool for managing emotional and behavioral problems like stress, anxiety, anger, relationship conflict, smoking and alcohol and drug dependency. Scientific research in recent years has documented the positive effects of relaxation on a variety of physical health problems such as asthma, irritable bowel syndrome, immune system dysfunction, diabetes, high blood pressure, heart attack, stroke, dermatological conditions, seizure disorders, sleep disorders, and painful musculoskeletal disorders such as fibrositis, myofacial pain syndrome, and fibromyalgia.

Learning to incorporate good relaxation skills into your daily life will reduce your suffering if you currently struggle with any of the conditions described above. In addition, however, learning and practicing the skill of relaxation can help prevent the development of chronic stress related physical disorders, behavioral problems, and emotional disturbance.

Much has been written in recent years about the value of preventative medicine and about the need for each of us to take personal responsibility for creating and maintaining our own health or wellness. The ability to recognize stress, both physical and emotional, and to use relaxation to manage our reactions to stress is a fundamental component of preventative medicine and personal wellness.

THE NUTSHELL

"Just the facts ma'am."
—Joe Friday
Dragnet

Relaxation is a skill that can significantly improve the quality of your life. Successful development and use of the skill of relaxation will result in improved physical and emotional health. In order to learn to use relaxation effectively in your life, in the beginning, some degree of practice is usually necessary. Fortunately, once you begin to get the hang of it, the time you spend practicing will be quite pleasant and enjoyable. After you have practiced the techniques described in this book for twenty or thirty minutes once or twice a day for anywhere from a week to a couple of months, you will develop the ability to achieve deep states of relaxation within a few minutes even in very stressful situations. Once you have developed the ability to relax rapidly you will no longer need to practice on a regular basis although you may decide that on occasion you will want to.

Two

Fundamentals

THE STRESS RESPONSE

"One of my problems is that I internalize everything.
I can't express anger; I grow a tumor instead."
—Woody Allen

Whenever we find ourselves in a situation in which we feel poorly prepared to meet the demands placed upon us, whether they are physical, emotional, interpersonal, or intellectual, a predictable set of physical, emotional, and mental reactions occur inside our bodies. This collection of reactions, which results primarily from the release of adrenaline into our blood, is called the stress response. It occurs when we feel physically or emotionally threatened, when we worry excessively, when we are in pain, when illness or pain threatens our life, livelihood, or lifestyle, when we fight with our friends or loved ones, when we feel anxious or angry, when we feel unable to resist the compulsion to drink, use drugs, or gamble, or when we feel alienated from our communities or our spiritual beliefs.

When the stress response gets triggered we are likely to experience one or more of the symptoms shown in the table on page 10. While this set of physical and mental reactions has increasingly been referred to as the stress response in recent years, you may also hear it referred to as the fight or flight response, or as the fight, flight, or freeze response. These names for the stress response were developed years ago because they describe why our bodies and minds react in the ways they do in stressful situations. In our ancient past, when we found ourselves in situations which threatened our lives or lifestyles we had a limited number of options for dealing with those situations. We might have fought for our lives, our property, our relation-ships, or our dignity. If we felt that fighting would be useless we might have tried to run away. In some situations, if we felt that we could not effectively fight or run away, our best strategy for avoiding danger may have been to "freeze" in the hope that our presence would not be noticed.

Symptoms of the Stress Response

Increased heart rate
Increased blood pressure
Rapid breathing
Sweating
Trembling
Mental confusion
Feelings of fear
Pre-occupation with possible dangers
Feelings of faintness
Increased muscle tension
Inability to get to sleep
Irritability
Digestive problems

While these reactions may have been very adaptive in the dim past, in today's world they are seldom effective in helping us to solve problems. If we work for a temperamental employer we cannot effectively manage the stress of that situation by picking a fight with the boss, by running away, or by holding perfectly still in the hope that he won't notice us. Similarly, the fight, flight, or freeze response is of little value in solving today's relationship conflicts or in reducing the stress associated with traffic jams, work, or long supermarket lines.

To make matters worse, the very fact that we are intelligent beings can work against us. Because we are capable of imagination, a real life stressor is not even necessary to trigger the stress response. We are able create imaginary threats in our minds even when no real threat exists. When we do this we still activate the stress response even though it is clearly unnecessary and inappropriate in such situations.

If we cannot turn off the stress response by fighting, fleeing, or freezing, we are then often left in a state of frequent or even perpetual stress which can take a severe toll on us both physically and mentally.

Chronic muscle tension can lead to recurrent or chronic muscle aches and pain. Chronic high blood pressure may lead to increased risk of heart disease and stroke. Chronic worry may lead to various anxiety disorders, sleepless nights, and disturbed digestion. Chronic stress has been demonstrated in scientific studies to increase the risk of illness, to reduce the length of survival for people with chronic life-threatening disease, to slow the healing of tissue following injury, and to generally reduce the effectiveness of the immune system.

THE RELAXATION RESPONSE

"…the Relaxation Response is a natural gift that anyone
can turn on and use."
—Herbert Benson
The Relaxation Response

Fortunately there are two sides to every coin. The flip side of the stress response is the relaxation response. The relaxation response is the human body's way of turning off the stress response. If we wanted to get technical we could talk about how the stress response is controlled by the sympathetic branch of the autonomic nervous system and the relaxation response represents the action of the parasympathetic branch of the autonomic nervous system. However, such a discussion is beyond the scope of this book. For now, all you really need to know is that the stress response and the relaxation response are firmly rooted in the way the nervous system works. Just as the stress response is the body's built-in system for self-protection, the relaxation response developed as the body's natural process for turning off the stress response once we had successfully disposed of the threat or danger through fighting, fleeing, or freezing.

Just as the stress response is an automatic response to our perception of danger, the relaxation response is an automatic response to our perception of safety. The reason we don't find it to be as easy to relax as we do to feel stressed is because we can no longer use the built-in behavioral strategies of fighting, fleeing, or freezing for reducing stress. If we could respond to most of the stressors in our lives by fighting or running away, once we had defeated our adversary or successfully escaped, the relaxation response would naturally take over without our having to think about it. Unfortunately, as we have seen, fighting and running away are usually not options in today's world. The result is overactivity of the stress response and underactivity of the relaxation response. The solution to this problem is to learn to bring the relaxation response under conscious control. To effectively manage stress in today's world we must learn to deliberately turn on the relaxation response.

PRACTICE

"It helps to keep at it"
—Jon Kabat-Zinn
Wherever You Go There You Are

Learning any new skill requires practice. Riding a bicycle, learning a new piece of music, or tying a new kind of knot are all examples of skills which require practice at first but which become automatic with enough repetition. The relaxation response is an automatically occurring process in the human body; however, the ability to turn it on deliberately is a skill, and skills require practice. If you wish to enjoy the tranquillity and peace of deep states of relaxation you will probably have to practice. If you wish to be able to consciously turn on the relaxation response so that you can relax rapidly in any of a variety of previously stressful situations you will probably have to practice even more. Fortunately, the practice of relaxation, when done with the proper attitude, is quite enjoyable.

To learn as rapidly as possible you should practice one or more of the strategies described in the next chapter twice a day for about half an hour each time. Your success at learning to relax will be directly related to how often you practice.

To assist you in your practice, detailed instructions which you can record on audio-cassette tapes have been provided in Chapter 5. Recording and then listening to these instructions will help you to stay focused in the beginning.

TRAINING WHEELS

"If you want a thing done well, do it yourself"
—Napoleon I

As children most of us learned the skill of riding a bicycle. Learning this skill was made easier for many of us because we had the benefit of a learning tool called training wheels. As long as we depended upon the training wheels, however, we really did not know how to ride; we knew how to ride only with the assistance of training wheels. We certainly would not have been comfortable just jumping on a neighbor's bike without training wheels and taking it for a spin. We might even have been reluctant to try to ride without the training wheels when our parents suggested that it was time. Nonetheless, it was only after we took the training wheels off our bicycles and discovered that we no longer needed them that we realized that we had truly begun to master the skill.

Relaxation is also a skill that must be learned. And, like learning to ride a bicycle, there are tools we can use to help us get started. However, just as we had to give up our training wheels so that we could master the skill of riding our bicycles, once we have learned enough about relaxation by using our learning tools we must leave them behind as well.

A good approach to learning relaxation is to begin by using an audiocassette tape for the first couple of weeks while you are learning the procedures. Once you become familiar with the relaxation procedures described on the tape and are able to achieve a deep state of relaxation on a fairly regular basis, you should begin practicing once a day with the tape and once

15

a day without the tape. Follow this routine until you are able to consistently achieve deep states of relaxation without the tape. Finally, you should quit using the tape altogether on a regular basis. You may still want to use it from time to time to refresh your memory, when you are feeling particularly stressed, or when you are having a difficult time staying focused.

Relaxation is something you need to be able to do to, and for, yourself. It is not something that this book will do for you or that a therapist, an audio-cassette tape, a doctor, a hypnotist, or biofeedback machinery can do for you. All of these can all be useful learning tools. They are the training wheels of relaxation. They can help you learn, but if you do not move beyond them at some point, they will actually prevent further learning and true mastery of the skill.

THE SETTING

"The nurse of full-grown souls is solitude".
—James Russell Lowed

Finding a suitable location in which to practice is very helpful. You will have greater success if you select a location that you find naturally relaxing and that is distraction free.

If you practice in your home, choose a quiet room and a comfortable chair, couch, or bed. Ask the other people who live in your home not to disturb you during your practice. If possible, turn off televisions and radios and unplug your phone. Don't practice while you have something cooking on the stove or if you are expecting visitors.

COMFORT

"Comfort is the only thing our civilization can give us"
—Oscar Wilde

Physical comfort is also very important at first. It is difficult to get very relaxed if you are not comfortable. In the beginning it is important to find a position, whether sitting or lying down, in which you feel as comfortable and supported as possible. Feel free to use pillows to increase your physical comfort. Be sure that your physical needs have been met. It's hard to relax if you are hungry or if you need to go to the bathroom.

As your level of skill increases you may wish to practice in positions or situations that are less comfortable in the interest of applying your skill to a wider variety of situations.

FOCUSED AWARENESS

"It helps to have a focus for your attention,
an anchor line to tether you to the present moment
and to guide you back when the mind wanders."
—Jon Kabat-Zinn
Wherever You Go There You Are

As you begin your practice of relaxation you will quickly come to be aware of the tendency of your mind to wander. This tendency, which we all have, to constantly be thinking about all manner of things can interfere with achieving much in the way of relaxation.

If you can find something to focus your mind upon you are less likely to think about things that will detract from your ability to achieve a state of deep relaxation.

You can focus your attention on something as simple as your breathing, a mental image, a word that you repeat to yourself, counting backward with each breath, or a question you are seeking insight into. It doesn't really matter what you choose to focus on. What you choose to focus on is not nearly as important as is ensuring that you choose to focus on something.

DEALING WITH DISTRACTION

"Empty yourself of everything. Let the mind rest at peace.
The ten thousand things rise and fall while the self watches their return.
They grow and flourish and then return to the source…"
-Lao Tsu
Tao Te Ching

Decide in the beginning that you are not going to be upset or frustrated by distractions. Distractions will arise within your own mind and body as well as from the outside world. Internal distractions include such things as your mind wandering and various thoughts or physical sensations. It is not unusual to find yourself thinking thoughts such as "This is a waste of time," "I'm no good at this," or to find yourself thinking about other things you need to do. In the same way, it is also not unusual to find yourself being distracted by unusual bodily sensations such as feeling lightheaded, disoriented, muscle twitches, or minor aches and pains.

Since it is almost certain that you will be distracted by internal and external events, it is very important that you begin with the attitude that when such distractions occur you will not react with frustration or impatience, but rather will gently and easily return to whatever you have chosen to focus your awareness upon. It is also important to understand that distraction is to be expected. People who are experienced at relaxation accept the fact that during their practice of relaxation they will at least occasionally, and often frequently, find themselves being distracted. It is just a part of the experience and nothing to be upset by. It is certainly not a barrier to effective practice and not a reason to give up. Remember that distraction is to be expected and that with practice, although it will never go away completely, it will become less bothersome.

Three

Techniques

TECHNIQUES

There are many strategies a person can use to become relaxed. In this chapter I will describe the physical relaxation strategies of breathing, progressive muscle relaxation, and stretching, and the mental strategies of autogenic suggestion, imagery, contemplation, meditation, prayer, and self-hypnosis.

There is a fair amount of overlap between the different relaxation techniques. For example, imagery can be a relaxation technique in its own right, but it can also be an important part of breathing exercises, autogenic suggestion, prayer, and meditation.

The fact that the dividing line between the various techniques is not always clear should not be a reason for concern or confusion. In fact, you will probably find that some combination of the techniques described in this chapter is more effective for you than are any of the individual techniques. As an example, many students of relaxation, myself included, favor a practice routine which follows the pattern below:

1) Begin with a few brief stretching exercises
2) Spend a few minutes doing deep breathing exercises which incorporate mental imagery
3) Do an autogenic suggestion exercise
4) Wind up your relaxation exercise with several minutes of imagery

As you read the following pages and experiment with the various approaches to relaxation, pay particular attention to the techniques which appeal to you right away. You will probably want to start with those strategies. However, do not be too quick to dismiss the other approaches. Although one or more of the relaxation strategies may seem strange to you at first, if you give them a chance you may find that you like them and that they work well for you.

Some of the techniques are more difficult than others. If one of them seems difficult at first, don't worry about it. Practice the other techniques which come more easily to you. You may wish to give the more difficult approach a try again later after you have developed some skill using the relaxation strategies that come to you more easily.

The most important thing is that you find an approach or combination of approaches that works well for you. Feel free to modify and change any or all of the techniques in any way that makes sense for you. The descriptions and instructions that follow are not hard and fast rules to be obeyed. You should think of them as general guidelines which you are free to modify and elaborate on as much as is necessary in order to make them work for you.

If you find that you feel strange or uncomfortable when you are first practicing any of the relaxation techniques, don't worry about it. You are probably just not accustomed to being deeply relaxed. With a bit of practice you will become familiar with the sensations associated with relaxation. The very sensations that seem strange at first may become cues that you can use to help yourself rapidly relax later on.

There is one exception to this piece of advice. If you have diabetes you should make sure that your glucose level is well within normal limits before you begin your daily practice of relaxation. For reasons that will not be explained here, relaxation can lower your blood sugar level. If you have diabetes you may also wish to keep some juice or a snack of some kind handy in case you start feeling hypoglycemic during your practice.

As you read each of the descriptions that follow, set the book down for a few minutes after each section and briefly practice what you have read. If you do this, you may be surprised to discover how much more relaxed you feel when you finish this chapter compared to how you feel right now.

BREATHING

A good place to start learning relaxation is with your breathing. Ironically, aside from times when we experience shortness of breath associated with anxiety or health problems such as asthma, we are rarely aware of how we breathe. There are a wide variety of breathing exercises that have been developed to assist in relaxation. Some are simple and some are more complicated. Some focus on controlling the way in which you breath. Others focus on awareness of the sensations associated with breathing.

A simple and very popular breathing technique is simply called deep breathing. You will also hear it referred to as diaphragmatic, abdominal, or belly breathing.

The instructions for deep breathing are quite simple:

Take slow deep rhythmical breaths which fill your lungs completely.

That's it. For various reasons, as people grow older they tend to develop the habit of breathing from their chests and not taking full abdominal breaths. To take a full breath you need to fill the lower parts of your lungs as well as the upper parts. To do so, however, requires a slower and fuller breath.

There is a simple way to see if you are breathing from your chest or from your diaphragm. Place one hand flat on your chest and the other just above your belly button. Watch your hands to see how much they move when you take a slow deep breath. You should practice breathing so that the hand on your belly moves in and out, while the hand on your chest does not move much at all. At first you may need to use your stomach muscles to help you push your abdomen out while you inhale and to suck it back in when you exhale.

By retraining your breathing in this manner you may begin to feel more relaxed within a matter of a few seconds and certainly within a matter of a few minutes. Some people are so unfamiliar with what it feels like to be relaxed that they may find that deep breathing feels uncomfortable to them. If you experience this problem, don't worry about it. Just stick with it and the feelings of discomfort will go away. If you feel lightheaded, again don't worry. This happens because you are getting more oxygen to your brain than you normally do.

You may find that it helps to count while you breathe. You may wish to begin by counting slowly to three or four as you inhale and exhale. Like this:

In...two...three...four, pause,
Out...two...three...four, pause

It's normal to pause briefly between inhaling and exhaling. As you become more comfortable with deep breathing you may wish to slow your breaths even more by counting to five and then to six, seven, or eight.

Deep breathing is a good place to start, but there are many variations on breathing exercises. A few variations that incorporate some physical activity include:

* Slowly and smoothly bending over from a sitting position while breathing out and slowly and smoothly sitting upright while breathing in. While doing this exercise your arms should hang limply at your sides.

* Stretching your arms out to your sides or up above your head while breathing in and slowly bringing them down to rest in your

lap while breathing out. Get a real good stretch when you do this. Make sure your movements and breaths are slow and smooth.

* Stretch your arms out to your sides as you breathe in, and as you breathe out cross your arms in front of you as though you are giving yourself a big hug. Do this slowly and smoothly.

There are also breathing exercises that incorporate imagery.

* Imagine that you can see the air you are breathing. Imagine that it is colored in some way that you choose. As you inhale, imagine that you see the air swirling around as it enters your nose and mouth and that you can see it flow down into your lungs where the air molecules are picked up by the blood and circulated to every inch of your body. Then continue to imagine what it looks like as the air is collected by the blood, returned to the lungs, and is exhaled out of your body. Some students of relaxation like to imagine that the air they breathe in is a soft, light color representing relaxation, peace, purity, health, and so on, while the air they breathe out is a different, darker color representing all of the tension and impurities the air has picked up on its trip through the body and which is expelled from the body with each breath.

* While inhaling slowly through your nose imagine that you are smelling a very delicate flower which is close to your face. Your breath brings the relaxing fragrance to you while just barely disturbing the petals of the flower.

* While breathing out slowly through your mouth imagine that you are blowing a thin stream of air at a candle flame that is near your face. Breathe in a manner that causes the candle flame to just flicker but not go out.

To get started on your practice of relaxation right now, pick one or more of the breathing strategies described above and practice each for five minutes. If you need to get away from distractions, go into another room. Close your eyes. Get as comfortable as you can. Focus all of your awareness on your breathing. Each time you are distracted, gently, calmly, and easily return your attention to your breathing. Each time you breathe out you may wish to silently repeat the word "relax" or some other calming word of your own choosing.

Progressive Muscle Relaxation

Progressive muscle relaxation is based on the idea that if you tense your muscles and then relax them, they will relax more than if you try to relax them without tensing them first. To demonstrate this to yourself do the following exercise. Concentrate for about twenty seconds on relaxing all of the muscles in your left hand and arm. Now without tensing any of the other muscles in your body, tense the muscles in your right hand and arm by making a fist and pumping up your bicep muscle. Hold the tension for ten seconds. Then relax your right arm. Notice the difference between how your right and left arms and hands feel. Your right arm and hand feel different from your left arm and hand because they are more relaxed.

This is a very popular technique with psychotherapists and stress management programs. The basic principles underlying the effectiveness of progressive muscle relaxation were described by Edmund Jacobson in the 1930's and many variations on the procedure have been developed since that time.

The basic procedure is to tense a group of muscles for several seconds and then to let that same group of muscles relax for several more seconds. While tensing a muscle group, you keep the rest of your body relaxed. You work gradually through all the muscles in your body in this way. Depending on what book you read, what therapist you see, or what stress management program you attend, the sequence of muscle groups that you tense and relax may vary. This is as it should be since there is no right or wrong way to do this or any other relaxation exercise. In the interest of learning, however, it is helpful to have some guidelines to follow. A useful sequence of muscle groups to try is shown in the table below.

Progressive Muscle Relaxation Sequence

1)	Hands
2)	Lower arms
3)	Upper arms
4)	Feet
5)	Lower legs
6)	Upper legs
7)	Abdomen
8)	Chest
9)	Shoulders
10)	Neck
11)	Mouth, throat, and jaw
12)	Eyes
13)	Forehead

Detailed instructions following this sequence are included in Chapter 5. Since this is a lot to remember, it may be useful for you to record the script in Chapter 5 on an audio-cassette tape so that you can listen to it while you practice until you have the sequence more or less memorized.

A good rule of thumb with progressive muscle relaxation is to tense each muscle group for about five to ten seconds and then relax the muscle group for about twenty to thirty seconds before moving on to the next muscle group. When you tense your muscles, create as much tension as you can without causing pain. Keep your attention focused on the physical sensations associated with tensing and relaxing. Remember that it is helpful to focus your attention on something for the purpose of calming your mind as well as your body. In the case of progressive muscle relaxation you focus your attention on the physical sensations associated with tensing and relaxing your muscles.

When you have finished the progressive muscle relaxation sequence you may wish to remain still for several minutes while you repeat a relaxing word with each breath, count backward, or engage in some pleasant imagery.

Once you are able to achieve a deep state of relaxation by using the thirteen muscle group sequence described above, you may wish to combine some of the muscle groups so that you tense only about half as many groups. For example, you might combine the hands and lower arms, the upper arms and chest, and so on. When you are able to achieve deep states of relaxation with the new, shorter sequence, you may wish to shorten it even more by first tensing and relaxing all the muscles in your upper body and then tensing and relaxing all the muscles in your lower body. Finally, you may wish to simply tense and then relax your entire body all at once.

STRETCHING

Stretching exercises for relaxation are a lot like progressive muscle relaxation. Both techniques involve a fair amount of physical activity and are focused much more on relaxing the muscles than the mind. Like progressive muscle relaxation, stretching exercises generally follow a sequence involving all of the major muscle groups in the body. The sequence that is followed in the stretching script in Chapter 5 is shown in the table below.

Stretching Sequence

1)	Hands
2)	Arms
3)	Feet
4)	Legs
5)	Abdomen and chest
6)	Shoulders
7)	Neck
8)	Face

Again, since this is a lot of information to remember it may be useful for you to record the script in Chapter 5 on an audio-cassette tape so that you can listen to it while you practice until you have the sequence more or less memorized. Feel free to change and modify the sequence and the specific stretching instructions if you think a different sequence or type of stretch makes more sense to you.

When you do the stretching exercises you should stretch each of the muscle groups in a very slow, smooth, and gentle manner until you feel a full, complete stretch in the muscle group you are focusing on.

To demonstrate this technique to yourself, slowly and gradually lift both of your arms and reach out in front of your body. Spread your fingers apart and get a good complete stretch in all of the muscles of your hands and arms. Hold the stretch for about ten seconds and then slowly and gradually relax your hands and arms. Notice the sensations in your hands and arms following the stretch. During the stretch all of your attention should be focused on the physical sensations associated with stretching and relaxing. Try to stretch only the muscles you are working on while keeping the rest of your body relaxed. Once you have achieved a full, complete stretch you then very slowly, smoothly, and gently relax the muscles you are working with. Allow yourself about five to ten seconds to complete the stretch, five to ten seconds to release the stretch, and about ten seconds before you repeat the stretch or move on to the next muscle group.

There are many ways to stretch a given muscle group. Feel free to experiment and to come up with a way of stretching your muscles that makes sense to you.

AUTOGENIC RELAXATION

Autogenic suggestion is a purely mental relaxation strategy. As with most of the of the other strategies discussed, there are a number of variations of autogenic suggestion. What they all have in common is that you use your mind to focus on physical changes or sensations in your body.

A very popular form of autogenic suggestion involves focusing your awareness on creating sensations of warmth and heaviness in the various muscle groups in your body. As was the case with progressive muscle relaxation and stretching, this is often done in a sequential manner. Following a sequence such as those described in the sections on stretching and progressive muscle relaxation is a good idea. Instead of tensing or stretching your muscles, however, you simply give yourself the suggestion that your muscles are feeling warm, heavy, and relaxed. Sensations of warmth and heaviness are commonly associated with increased relaxation and as such, if you can cultivate these feelings in your muscles, your muscles are likely to relax.

Autogenic suggestion is an exercise that clearly illustrates the connection between your mind and your body. If you are open to the experience you will discover that by simply giving yourself instructions or suggestions that you are going to feel something, your body will go along with the program and actually produce the suggested sensations.

The originator of this technique, Dr. H. H. Shultz, suggested a number of autogenic suggestions you can use:

* Focusing on a feeling of heaviness in your arms and legs
* Focusing on a feeling of warmth in your arms and legs

* Focusing on increasing and decreasing your heart rate
* Passive concentration on your breathing
* Cultivation of feelings of coolness in your forehead

Jonathan C. Smith describes an autogenic technique he calls mental massage in which you imagine that the various muscle groups in your body are being massaged.

Whether you are focusing on feelings of warmth, heaviness, or massage, the basic strategy is the same. You simply focus all your awareness on a specific body part—the hands for example—and repeatedly and passively give yourself instructions such as:

> My hands are becoming warm and heavy...
> warm and heavy...
> relaxing...letting go...
> melting away the tension...
> warm and heavy...

As you let these phrases repeat over and over in your mind you imagine sensations of warmth, heaviness, and relaxation in your hands. Continue to let the phrase "My hands are becoming warm and heavy" repeat itself over and over in a very calm and passive manner for a minute or more. Then move on to the next muscle group changing the focus of your awareness and the phrase you repeat so that your attention is directed to the next muscle group, for example:

> My forearms are becoming warm and heavy......
> warm and heavy...
> relaxing...letting go...
> melting away the tension...
> warm and heavy...

Following this same strategy you move slowly and gradually through all of the muscles in your body.

You may find that including some imagery in your autogenic suggestion exercises is quite helpful. For example, if you are focusing on cultivating feelings of warmth you may imagine that you are sitting in a hot bath or relaxing at a hot springs resort. If you are cultivating feelings of heaviness, you may imagine that you are sinking comfortably into the chair or bed you are relaxing on.

Remember that as you focus on repeating the autogenic phrases and on creating the physical sensations of warmth and heaviness that it is quite likely that your mind will wander or be distracted. Expect this to happen. Do not let it upset or frustrate you. Simply notice that you were distracted and gently and easily return your mind to focusing on the phrases you are repeating and the physical sensations you are cultivating.

An autogenic suggestion relaxation script suitable for you to record is included in Chapter 5. Feel free to modify the script in any way that makes sense to you.

MENTAL IMAGERY

Perhaps one of the most enjoyable approaches to relaxation is the use of imagery techniques. By now you will not be surprised to learn that there are many variations on this technique as well. The number of different types of imagery you can engage in is limited only by your imagination. Different types of imagery have been developed in recent years for almost every specific form of emotional and physical problem conceivable.

To get a feel for how imagery works, turn now to the imagery script in Chapter 5 and read through it. Close your eyes periodically while you are reading the script so that you may vividly imagine the images described in the script. Doing this now will help you to understand the discussion which follows.

When you use imagery for general relaxation it works best if you focus your complete attention on the scene you are imagining. It is also important to involve all of your senses as fully as you can. Once you have decided upon an image to focus on you should thoroughly explore the sights, sounds, physical sensations, smells, and tastes associated with the image. Each time you get distracted, calmly return your attention to your imagery.

Your imagery can be whatever you want it to be, but for it to be most effective you should choose imagery that you find relaxing and comforting. Imagery involving physically exciting activities will probably not be as effective as more passive and relaxing imagery.

Common imagery themes include imagining that you are resting in a beautiful mountain meadow, seeing the view from a mountain top, reclining in a hammock hung between two trees near a cabin and a lake, or lying on a beach on a warm summer day.

Remember to fully involve all of your senses in your experience of the images that you conjure up. Remember not to be bothered by distraction, but rather simply return your focus of attention to your imagery each time you are distracted. If you want to make the imagery more elaborate, after fully exploring the sights, sounds, physical sensations, smells, and tastes, you can imagine how some or all of these sensory experiences change over the course of a day, a season, or a year.

CONTEMPLATION

Contemplation is a very passive form of mental relaxation in which you focus all your awareness on an object or topic of interest for the purpose of developing a greater understanding or appreciation of whatever it is that you choose to focus upon.

During contemplation of an object you simply look at the object or imagine it in your mind's eye. You examine the object from every possible perspective and let whatever thoughts or images you may have about the object simply come to mind. You do not think about or analyze the object or the ideas and images that come to mind related to the object. You simply notice what comes to mind and then let go of the thought or image so that it can be replaced by whatever thought or image emerges next.

When the focus of your contemplation is a real or imagined object you look at the shape of the object, the outline, the highlights and shadows, the texture, reflections, and colors. You contemplate how the object looks from the front view, from the sides, from behind, from different distances, and at different times of day. You may even contemplate what it would be like to be the object. While examining the object in these various ways thoughts about the object and images and memories will come automatically to mind. Simply attend to these thoughts, images, and memories but do not think about them. Simply notice them and then let them go and wait to see what thoughts, images, memories, or feelings replace them.

Contemplation can also be used as a way to develop a greater understanding of a problem or issue in your life. When using contemplation for this purpose, instead of focusing your attention on an object, you focus

41

your awareness on, and continually return your awareness to, the issue or topic of your contemplation. For example, at some point you may wish to use contemplation to explore the question of what sensations, images, memories, or words might help you to relax more rapidly or more deeply. To do this you would simply repeat a question such as:

What physical sensations, images, and/or words
do I associate with being deeply relaxed?
or
What is relaxing to me right now?

Then, while gently, quietly, and calmly letting the phrase repeat itself over and over in your mind, you simply pay attention to the thoughts, images, and words that automatically come to mind.

Almost anything can be the object of your contemplation: everyday objects, works of art, things that occur naturally in nature, a friend or loved one, a problem, a question, or an issue of some interest to you.

Remember that during your periods of contemplation you will be distracted from time to time and that this is to be expected. Simply return your awareness calmly and easily to the object of your contemplation over and over again. Gradually, you will find that you are distracted less frequently and are able to spend more time in a state of deep relaxation.

MEDITATION

Meditation is similar to contemplation. The difference is that in meditation you do not seek to gain a greater understanding of whatever you choose to focus your attention upon as is the case in contemplation. Rather, in meditation, your goal is simply to focus your attention on something without thinking about it at all. Any thoughts which occur to you are simply treated as a distraction. Meditation in a sense is nothing but continually returning from distraction. Without distraction it would not be meditation.

Two general approaches to meditation have been described by Dr. Jonathan C. Smith in his book *Relaxation Dynamics*. While there are actually many types of meditation that have been described over the past several thousand years, many of these approaches can be grouped into one of Dr. Smith's two categories: Centered Focus Meditation and Open Focus Meditation.

One approach to centered focus meditation is to simply choose a word to repeat over and over to yourself in your mind. If you wish, and the situation permits it, you can say the word out loud. Whether you say the word to yourself or you say it out loud, you should repeat it in a gentle, relaxing manner and imagine it echoing in your mind. You make no effort to think about the word or about anything else. Every time you are distracted you gently and easily return to focusing on the word you have selected.

As an alternative, you may wish to focus upon an object such as a candle flame or a picture or you may choose to focus upon a mental image of such an object.

In open focus meditation, instead of focusing on a specific word, image, or object, you open your awareness and attend to everything you see, hear, feel, taste, smell, or think. You make no effort to think about or analyze any of the things you experience. You simply keep your awareness open to anything you might experience. Let the thoughts, feelings, sounds, and sensations come and go of their own accord. Don't attempt to think about them or push them away. Simply experience them as they are.

Readers who are interested in learning more about meditation will find the book *Wherever You Go There You Are* by Dr. Jon Kabat-Zinn very useful.

PRAYER

Prayer is an effective and often overlooked approach to relaxation. Much has been written about prayer in the past two thousand years and prayer has much in common with the techniques of meditation, contemplation, and imagery. The primary difference is that prayer has a decidedly spiritual component.

There are several approaches to prayer. Perhaps the most common form of prayer, and the one most people are familiar with, is the prayer of supplication or intercession. In this type of prayer we ask God for a blessing or for assistance of some kind. The phrase "God Bless Mommy and Daddy" is a prayer of supplication as is the "Now I lay me down to sleep, I pray the Lord my soul to keep" prayer that many of us learned in childhood. Prayers of supplication, in and of themselves, will not help you to develop your relaxation skills. Fortunately, you can take your efforts at prayer beyond supplication to contemplation and meditation and in so doing enrich your spiritual life while at the same time learning to relax your mind and body.

In meditative prayer you focus your awareness entirely on a sacred word, phrase, object, or image that in some way partakes of, or represents, the deity of your spiritual tradition. An example of meditative prayer is repetition of words of praise to God. During this type of prayer you focus your awareness entirely on the phrase you are repeating. As such, this type of prayer is quite similar to centered focus meditation. The primary difference is that the object of meditative prayer is a word, phrase, object, or image which is sacred to the person who is praying.

An example of a phrase from the Christian Bible which might be used in meditative prayer is:

"Be still and know that I am God"

Of course, meditative prayer is not limited to any particular faith. Anyone can meditate upon sacred words, phrases, objects, or images no matter what his or her religious or spiritual tradition.

The history of the world's religions also reveals that for thousands of years people have engaged in a variation of prayer which we might call contemplative prayer. This type of prayer is similar to the relaxation technique of contemplation described earlier. The difference is that in contemplative prayer the object of your contemplation again is something which is sacred to your spiritual tradition. Contemplative prayer goes beyond meditative prayer in that contemplative prayer adds the element of listening for divinely revealed knowledge.

Throughout history people have used contemplative prayer to develop a greater awareness and understanding of deities such as Allah, Brahma, God, Krishna, or Wankan Tanka, or of a prophet such as Jesus or Mohammed. You might use a picture or other religious object as the object of your contemplative prayer or visualize the picture or religious object in your mind. Contemplative prayer has also been used to help achieve and understand experiences such as Buddhahood, Enlightenment, Grace, or Nirvana. For example, you might contemplate the question:

"How do I sense the presence of God?"

And then attend to the images, sensations, thoughts, and memories that are revealed to you.

Another contemplative approach to prayer which might be pursued for the purpose of gaining a richer understanding of religious writings is to focus your contemplative prayer on a passage from a religious or sacred text.

Historically, people have engaged in meditative and contemplative prayer not for the purpose of relaxation, but rather for the purpose of increasing their understanding of their religion or spiritual tradition, or for achieving an experience of connection with a spiritual deity or reality. Such experiences do, however, bring with them a wonderful sense of peace of mind and physical relaxation. As such, if religion or spirituality is an important part of your life, contemplative prayer and meditative prayer may be excellent approaches for you to use in developing your skill at relaxation while at the same time nurturing your religious or spiritual development.

Many religious and spiritual traditions encourage their followers to attempt to cultivate, through prayer, the ability to maintain a sense of communion with God at all times. In Christianity this is known as achieving a state of grace and in Buddhism as achieving nirvana. To be able to achieve and maintain such a state of communion can be thought of as the spiritual equivalent of developing the ability to keep the relaxation response turned on all of the time.

SELF-HYPNOSIS

Hypnosis is often defined as an altered state of consciousness in which a person has a heightened receptiveness to suggestion. When used for relaxation, self-hypnosis incorporates elements of imagery and autogenic suggestion. As is the case with all of the mental relaxation techniques, the use of narrowly focused attention, in this case on the self-hypnotic instructions, and a passive attitude toward distraction is extremely important.

To use self-hypnosis for relaxation it is helpful to initially use a recorded script. An example of a script suitable for recording is included in Chapter 5.

One of the characteristics of self-hypnosis that may seem unique is the ability to use what are called post-hypnotic suggestions to help yourself recall the hypnotic state rapidly after you have gone through the full script one or more times.

If you turn to the self-hypnosis script in Chapter 5 you will see that near the end of the script there is a suggestion that by lightly grasping your left wrist with your right hand while counting your breaths backward from ten to one, you will be able to rapidly experience a sense of muscular relaxation throughout your body as well as a calming of the activity of your mind. This is an example of a post-hypnotic suggestion.

It could be argued that this use of post-hypnotic suggestion is really not much different from the techniques of recall and cue controlled relaxation which are discussed in the next chapter. It could also be argued that in self-hypnosis the mechanism of action in bringing on the state of rapid relaxation is an unconscious process while in cue controlled and recall relaxation the mechanism of action is a conscious process. For our purposes, however, this argument is not important. What is important is whether or not you find the idea of using post-hypnotic suggestions to help you achieve rapid relaxation appealing. Many people are intrigued and fascinated by hypnosis and feel quite at ease about the idea of putting themselves into a hypnotic trance during which they give themselves suggestions that will enable them to rapidly become relaxed in the future. On the other hand, there are also many people who are not comfortable with idea of being hypnotized and who would prefer to consciously use the approaches of recall and cue controlled relaxation for achieving rapid relaxation. Both approaches lead to the same goal of rapid relaxation and both approaches work. It is simply a matter of whether one approach is more appealing to you than the other. For many people both approaches will be of interest. If you are one of these people, your knowledge of, and skill at, achieving deep states of prolonged restful relaxation as well as rapid, on the spot relaxation will be enhanced by learning both techniques.

Four

Fine Tuning

QUIETING

Breathing exercises, progressive muscle relaxation, and stretching exercises all involve some physical activity that has the direct effect of relaxing your muscles. Autogenic suggestion, imagery, contemplation, meditation, prayer, and self-hypnosis are predominately mental in nature and as such involve little or no physical activity. Since this is the case, it is often helpful to engage in a bit of physical relaxation prior to using these mental techniques. This introductory physical activity has been called the quieting reflex because it has the effect of quieting physical tension you may be experiencing prior to your practice of a mental relaxation technique.

The quieting reflex can be accomplished by using one or more of the breathing, tensing, or stretching exercises described in Chapter 3. Spending a few minutes engaging in one or more of those types of exercises prior to beginning the more mental techniques is highly recommended and will almost certainly lead to a more satisfying and effective experience with the mental techniques.

The combination relaxation technique described on page 25 included a sequence of quieting activities. If you refer to that discussion you will see that the sequence begins with a few stretches followed by some deep breathing. These exercises are the quieting sequence which is then followed by more extensive work with autogenic suggestion and imagery.

Recall Relaxation

In the beginning you may wish to use audio-cassette tapes to assist you in learning some of the approaches to relaxation described in the previous chapter. However, once you have learned to achieve a fairly deep state of relaxation and are reasonably familiar with the instructions for doing so, it will be important for you to work on developing the ability to induce the state of relaxation without the assistance of the tapes.

In recall relaxation you use your memory of what the relaxed state feels like to guide your practice. Recall relaxation is most effectively used in conjunction with progressive muscle relaxation or stretching exercises. As soon as you feel that you are able to recall either of those relaxation procedures, and you also feel that you have made some good progress in achieving a reasonably deep state of relaxation, it will be time to begin practicing recall relaxation.

To practice recall relaxation you mentally run through the same muscle groups you would normally tense or stretch, but instead of tensing or stretching your muscles, simply recall what those muscles have felt like in the past after you have tensed or stretched them and imagine those sensations returning.

To help yourself learn to do this, pay attention to the physical sensations that you experience during the progressive muscle relaxation or stretching exercises and give names to those sensations such as warm, cool, light, heavy, limp, tingling, and so on. Then when you practice recall relaxation you simply imagine your muscles becoming warm, limp, and tingling, or whatever set of physical sensations you have experienced after actually tensing or stretching your muscles. Spend a minute or two cultivating the sensations in one muscle group and then move on to the next muscle group until you have relaxed your entire body.

CUE CONTROLLED RELAXATION

Cue controlled relaxation is the most important step in developing the ability to relax very rapidly in stressful situations. With cue controlled relaxation you learn to turn on the relaxation response in situations which are not naturally relaxing. In order to do this you associate one or more cues with the state of deep relaxation. Then, by bringing those cues to mind you trigger the relaxation response in situations in which the stress response had been automatically triggered in the past.

If you pay attention during your regular practice of relaxation you will find that there are particular physical sensations or mental images which you become aware of while you are deeply relaxed. These sensations and images can serve as useful cues. You may wish to use the contemplation strategy to help you become aware of useful sensations and images. The particular sensations and images that occur differ from person to person but there is enough similarity across individuals to give you some suggestions of commonly experienced physical sensations.

Feelings of warmth, coolness, heaviness, or lightness are common. Loss of awareness of the position of your arms or legs is also common. Many people report that when they are deeply relaxed they cannot tell if their hands are crossed in their lap, uncrossed and lying on their legs, or hanging at their sides. Some people report various kinds of visual imagery or pleasant memories which occur spontaneously.

Once you are able to achieve deep states of relaxation, begin spending a few minutes near the end of your practice period focusing on whatever physical sensations or mental images are occurring during your practice. If you feel warm and heavy throughout your body while relaxed, then begin focusing on those sensations. If you spontaneously experience any kind of visual phenomenon while deeply relaxed, begin focusing on those visual experiences during your practice. These physical and mental experiences will then become the cues which will help you bring on the state of deep relaxation rapidly in situations in which you do not normally feel relaxed.

It is also helpful to deliberately create a verbal cue that you repeat over and over to yourself while you are deeply relaxed. Words that are commonly used by students of relaxation include "relax," "let go," "out," "deeper," "peace," "comfort," and so on. You can select any word you wish, but be sure that it is a word that conveys feelings of relaxation for you.

As a result of spending a fair amount of time focusing on your verbal, physical, and mental cues, you will discover that your cues can help you achieve deep states of relaxation more rapidly during your normal practice routine. You will also find that you can use your cues to help you relax quickly in a wide variety of stressful situations.

By simply using your cue word and recalling the physical and mental sensations associated with relaxation, you will be able to turn off the stress response whenever the events of the day may trigger it. If you find yourself feeling tense at work, angry at someone, anxious, in pain, disconnected from others or the world, at risk for smoking or drinking or using drugs, or spiritually or existentially lost, and you cannot sit or lie down for twenty minutes, by repeating your cue word, taking a few deep breaths, and recalling the sensations you associate with relaxation, you will be able to become deeply relaxed in a matter of minutes.

I have provided a form at the back of the book for you to record possible relaxation cues so that it will be easy for you to remember them and to refer back to them while you are first learning to relax.

An example of how cue controlled relaxation can be used in daily life is called restroom relaxation. As the name suggests, it is an approach to rapid relaxation that is, at least sometimes, performed in the bathroom. As an example, imagine you are in a meeting at work and you are getting very tense and angry because of the content of the discussion. To practice rest-room relaxation you would excuse yourself to use the restroom. Once you are in the stall in the restroom you would spend a few minutes using your relaxation cues to shut off the stress response so that you can return to the meeting a few minutes later feeling more composed and less tense and angry. Of course, you don't need to remove yourself from the stressful sit-uation to practice cue controlled relaxation. With practice you will be able to use this skill to keep your body relaxed and your mind clear while you remain in stressful situations.

Once you have developed the ability to use cue controlled relaxation effectively you may choose to discontinue your regular routine of one or two twenty minute sessions of formal daily practice. For many people this may be the goal. Not everyone wants to make a commitment to setting aside twenty minutes twice a day for formal practice, although continued practice on a daily basis does clearly have its advantages. If you wish to dis-continue your daily practice once you are able to make effective use of cue controlled relaxation you should do so. You will probably find, however, that occasional booster sessions of practice lasting twenty or thirty min-utes will help you to maintain your skill.

DEEPENING

Once you have completed one of the relaxation techniques described in the previous chapter, you may wish to spend some additional time increasing the depth of your state of relaxation through the use of what are called deepening techniques.

A deepening technique can be as simple as mentally repeating a word or phase over and over that has the effect of enhancing your experience of relaxation. Examples of words and phrases commonly used for the purpose of deepening one's state of relaxation include "deeper," "letting go more and more," "with each breath—deeper and deeper," "more and more relaxed," "with each breath twice as relaxed." Counting backward with each breath also works well, particularly if you imagine an ever increasing sensation of warmth or sinking or muscular relaxation with each breath.

Common deepening imagery includes walking, almost floating, down a long stairway or a country, mountain, or beach front path. Again, it is useful to pair each step down with a breath and it is also useful to repeat a word that has a deepening effect with each breath and imaginary step. Some people like to imagine that they are floating away from all of their cares and worries on a cloud and that with each breath they are carried further and further away.

These are just some suggestions. With a bit of practice you will learn what type of deepening words, phrases, or images work well for you. Feel free to make up your own. Use contemplation to help you discover effective approaches to deepening. Remember that there is no right or wrong way to relax or to deepen your state of relaxation. What is important is that you feel the freedom to experiment and discover what works best for you.

Summing Up

That's it. Now you know everything you need to know to become highly skilled at relaxation. All you need is a bit of practice. Even without the scripts and forms which follow in the next sections of the book, you can begin practicing and using the relaxation strategies of breathing, prayer, contemplation, and meditation. Of course, you may wish to refer to the sections on those topics from time to time as well as to the sections on the setting, physical comfort, focused awareness, dealing with distraction, quieting, and deepening if you find that you are running into problems becoming as relaxed as you would like.

The scripts in the next chapter are intended to help you get started with the more complicated techniques of autogenic suggestion, progressive muscle relaxation, self-hypnosis, and mental imagery. Simply reading through the scripts may provide you with all the information you need to begin practicing those approaches. However, the scripts have deliberately been written so that you may record them on audio-cassette tapes.

But why not begin your formal practice of relaxation right now? If you have not already done so, take ten minutes or so right now to practice one or more of the relaxation approaches of breathing, imagery, prayer, meditation, or contemplation. Review the section in Chapter 3 on the approach you wish to try and then fill in the information in the first and third column of the Relaxation Practice Recording Form in Chapter 6. Then do nothing but focus your attention using the strategy you have chosen for ten minutes or so. Remember to stick with it for the full ten minutes and to not allow yourself to become upset by the fact that you get distracted. When you are finished, use the Relaxation Practice Recording Form to document the amount of time you spent in this exercise and the depth of relaxation you achieved.

Remember, with consistent practice of relaxation and development of the ability to turn on the relaxation response at will through the use of cue controlled relaxation in stressful situations, you will be well on your way to improved physical and mental health.

Five

Scripts

READING

If you decide to record one or more of the scripts in this chapter there are a few things you should keep in mind to help you make the most useful and effective recording possible.

* Read the script out loud a few times before you record it so that you are familiar with the words and phrases and so that you won't stumble over any of the words when you record it. This will also allow you to experiment with the tone of voice and rhythm you want to use.

* Read the script to someone else so that they can give you feedback.

* Make a new recording if you don't like the first one you make.

* Have someone you care deeply about and who cares deeply about you record the script.

* Speak slowly, much slower than you would in normal conversation.

* Play some soft music that you like in the background loud enough for it to be heard on the tape, but not so loud to interfere with your ability to concentrate on the instructions on the tape.

* When you see the following symbol..., pause for a second or more before continuing. I find that taking a slow deep breath provides just about the right length of a pause. Read the scripts slowly and allow frequent, brief pauses so that when you listen to the tape later you will have adequate time to process the information, and to experience the sensations associated with relaxation.

* Although the instructions in several of the scripts assume you are in a seated position, feel free to modify the instructions as necessary if you prefer to practice relaxation while lying down.

PROGRESSIVE MUSCLE RELAXATION SCRIPT

Before presenting the progressive muscle relaxation script there are a few things which will be helpful for you to know.

If you are currently experiencing pain in any part of your body you should tense the muscles in those areas just enough to feel an increase in tension, but not enough to cause pain.

Remember that there is no right or wrong way to do this exercise beyond following the basic instruction of tensing and then relaxing all of the muscles in your body. In writing the script which follows I have drawn from several sources and included several modifications based upon my personal preferences, experiences with relaxation, and work with clients in my psychotherapy practice. Just as I feel the freedom to create a sequence that makes sense to me, if you feel so inclined, you should do the same.

When you record the following script, or if you have someone read it to you, remember the following points.

Let the emphasis in your voice vary along with the exercise. When the instruction is to tense a muscle group your voice should be just a bit more intense. When the instruction is to relax a muscle group your voice should be more relaxed.

Time the tensing and relaxing cycles so that you spend between five and ten seconds tensing a muscle group and twenty to thirty seconds relaxing before you tense the next muscle group. Watch the second hand on your watch or on a clock while you are making your recording to be sure that you allow enough time. Resist the urge to speed up the script. We all have a natural tendency to not pause long enough between tensing cycles. Although it may seem almost unbearably slow to you while you are making the recording, you will appreciate the slow pace when you are listening to the recording while practicing.

Keep these suggestions in mind while you record the script which follows.

*　　　　　*　　　　　*

Begin to settle down by getting into a comfortable, seated position. Close your eyes and sit quietly for a few seconds while you begin to become aware of how your body feels.

Notice your hands..., How do they feel?..., Do they feel tense or loose?..., warm or cool?..., light or heavy?..., Now, build up the tension in your hands by making fists..., Keep the rest of your body relaxed while you hold the tension in your hands and notice what it feels like..., Hold it..., Hold it..., And now relax your hands and let them rest in your lap or at your sides..., Notice the changes in the sensations in your hands as the tension begins to drain away.

...Pause for twenty seconds...

Now, do it again. Build up the tension in your hands by making fists..., Remember not to tense any other part of your body..., Hold the tension in your hands and notice what it feels like..., Hold it..., Hold it..., And now relax your hands and let them rest in your lap or at your sides. For the next several seconds let your hands relax further and further while you pay attention to the sensations associated with your hands relaxing..., Are your hands warmer or cooler?..., Is there a tingling sensation?..., Make a mental note of whatever you feel in your hands now so that you will remember what relaxation feels like for you..., You may wish to imagine the tension draining down through your hands, out your finger tips, and away from your body...,

...Pause for twenty seconds...

Good..., Now, notice the muscles of your lower arms..., How do they feel?..., Are they relaxed or tense?..., warm or cool?..., light or heavy?..., Build up the tension in your lower arms now by pointing your fingers in toward your elbows. Do not tense any other part of your body..., Hold the tension in your lower arms and notice what it feels like..., Hold it..., Hold it..., And now relax your arms and again let your hands rest in your lap or at your sides..., Notice the changes in the sensations in your arms as the tension drains away.

...Pause for twenty seconds...

Now build up the tension in your lower arms again but this time by pointing your fingers at your head while the palms of your hands face away from you..., Remember not to tense any other part of your body..., Hold the tension in your arms and notice what it feels like..., Hold it..., Hold it..., And now relax and again let your hands rest in your lap or at your sides..., Notice the changes in the sensations in your arms as the tension drains away. Again, you may wish to imagine that the tension is draining down through your arms, your hands and your fingers, out of your body, and away from you.

...Pause for twenty seconds...

Now notice your upper arms..., How do they feel?..., Are they tense or relaxed?..., light or heavy?..., warm or cool?..., Build up the tension in your upper arms now by pulling your arms back and into your sides until you get a good, complete squeeze. Remember to keep the rest of your body relaxed…, Hold the tension in your upper arms and notice what it feels like…, Hold it…, Hold it…, And now relax and let your hands rest in your lap or at your sides…, Notice the changes in the sensations in your arms as the tension drains away.

…Pause for twenty seconds…

Good…, Now, tense your upper arms again by pulling your arms back and into your sides while remembering not to tense any other part of your body…, Hold the tension in your upper arms and notice what it feels like…, What words would you use to describe what you feel?…, Hold the tension…, Hold it…, And now relax and again let your hands rest in your lap or at your sides…, Notice the changes in the sensations in your upper arms as the tension drains away…, What words would you use to describe how your arms feel now?

…Pause for twenty seconds…

Now notice your feet…, How do they feel?…, Tense?…, loose?…, relaxed?…, warm?…, cool?…, light?…, heavy?…, Build up the tension in your feet now by curling your toes under as if you were holding a pencil with your foot. Remember not to tense any other part of your body…, Hold the tension in your feet and notice what it feels like…, Hold it…, Hold the tension…, And now relax your feet and let them rest comfortably on the floor…, Notice how the sensations in your feet change as the tension drains away.

…Pause for twenty seconds…

Now tense your feet again by curling your toes under as if you were holding a pencil with your foot…, Remember to keep the rest of your body relaxed…, Hold the tension in your feet and pay attention to what it feels like..., Hold it..., Hold it..., And now relax your feet and let them rest comfortably on the floor. How would you describe the changes in the sensations in your feet as the tension drains away?..., Again, you may enjoy imagining that the tension is draining down through your feet..., out of your toes..., and away from your body.

...Pause for twenty seconds...

Now notice your lower legs..., How do they feel?..., Build up the tension in your lower legs now by pointing your toes toward your upper body..., Hold the tension in your lower legs and notice what it feels like..., Hold the tension..., Hold it..., And relax, and let your feet again rest comfortably on the floor..., Notice the changes in the sensations in your legs as the tension drains down and away.

...Pause for twenty seconds...

Tense your lower legs again by pointing your toes toward your upper body. Remember not to tense any other part of your body..., Hold the tension in your lower legs and notice what it feels like..., Hold it..., Hold the tension..., And now relax and let your feet rest comfortably on the floor. Notice the changes in the sensations in your legs as the tension drains down from your lower legs, through your feet, out of your toes, and away from your body.

...Pause for twenty seconds...

Now notice your upper legs..., How do they feel?..., Are they tense or relaxed?..., warm or cool?..., light or heavy?..., Now, build up the tension in your upper legs by pulling your knees together and lifting your legs off the chair while keeping the rest of your body relaxed..., Hold the tension in your upper legs and notice what it feels like..., How would you describe it?..., Hold it..., Hold the tension..., And then relax and let your feet again rest comfortably on the floor. Notice any changes in the sensations in your legs as the tension drains away.

…Pause for twenty seconds…

Now tense your upper legs again by pulling your knees up and together..., Hold the tension in your upper legs and notice what it feels like..., Hold the tension..., Hold it..., And now relax and let your feet rest comfortably on the floor. Notice the changes in the sensations in your legs as the tension drains down from your upper legs, through your lower legs and feet, and out through your toes away from your body.

…Pause for twenty seconds…

Good..., Now, notice your abdomen..., How do the muscles in your abdomen feel?..., Build up the tension in your abdomen now by sucking your stomach in as far as you can..., While keeping the rest of your body relaxed, hold the tension in your abdomen and notice what it feels like..., Hold it..., Hold the tension..., And then relax..., Just let go and notice how the sensations in your abdomen change as the tension drains away.

…Pause for twenty seconds…

Now build up the tension in your abdomen again, but this time by pushing your stomach out as far as you can..., Keep the rest of your body relaxed..., Hold the tension in your abdomen and notice what it feels like..., Hold it..., Hold the tension..., And then relax..., Just let go..., There is nothing for you to do but to notice the changes in the sensations in your abdomen as the tension drains down and away.

…Pause for twenty seconds…

Now notice the sensations in the muscles of your chest..., How do those muscles feel?..., Build up the tension in your chest by taking in a deep, full breath and holding it..., While keeping the rest of your body relaxed, hold the tension in your chest and notice what it feels like..., Hold it..., Hold it..., And then relax..., Just let go and notice the changes in the sensations in your chest as the tension drains away.

...Pause for twenty seconds...

And build up the tension in your chest again by taking in a deep breath and holding it while keeping the rest of your body relaxed..., Hold the tension in your chest and notice what it feels like..., Hold it..., Hold it..., And now relax..., Just let go and once again notice the changes in the sensations in your chest as the tension drains away.

...Pause for twenty seconds...

Now notice the sensations in the muscles of your shoulders..., How do those muscles feel?..., Create tension in your shoulders now by shrugging them up toward your head..., Keep the rest of your body relaxed while you hold the tension in your shoulders and notice what it feels like..., Hold the tension..., Hold it..., And relax..., Let go and just notice the changes in the sensations in your shoulders as the tension drains away.

...Pause for twenty seconds...

Tense your shoulders again by shrugging them up toward your head..., Remember to keep the rest of your body relaxed while you hold the tension in your shoulders..., Notice what it feels like..., Hold it..., Hold the tension in your shoulders..., And then relax..., Let go and notice the changes in the sensations in your shoulders as the tension drains away.

...Pause for twenty seconds...

Very good..., Now notice the sensations in the muscles of your neck..., How does your neck feel?..., Create tension in the muscles of your neck now by pulling your chin down toward your chest, while at the same time pushing backward with the back of your neck..., Keep the rest of your body relaxed while you hold the tension in your neck and notice what it feels like..., Hold it..., Hold it..., And relax..., Let go..., Let go and notice the changes in the sensations in your neck as the tension drains away.

...Pause for twenty seconds...

Now, build up the tension in the muscles of your neck again, this time by squeezing the back of your head into your shoulders..., Keep the rest of your body relaxed and notice what the tension feels like..., Hold the tension in your neck..., Hold it..., And let go..., Just let your neck muscles relax..., Let go and notice the changes in the sensations in your neck as the tension drains away.

...Pause for twenty seconds...

Now notice the sensations in the muscles around your mouth, jaw, and throat..., What do you sense in those muscles?..., Are they tight or relaxed?..., hard or smooth?..., Create tension in those muscles now by clenching your teeth and forcing the corners of your mouth out into a wide smile..., Keep the rest of your body relaxed while you hold the tension in your mouth, jaw, and throat..., Notice what the tension feels like..., Hold it..., Hold it..., And relax..., Let go..., Just relax..., Remember, there is nothing for you to do but to quietly notice the changes in the sensations in your mouth, jaw, throat, and the rest of your body as the tension continues to drain away.

…Pause for twenty seconds…

Now, build up the tension in the same muscles again by clenching your teeth and forcing the corners of your mouth out into a wide smile…, Keep the rest of your body relaxed while you hold the tension in your mouth, jaw, and throat…, Notice what the tension feels like…, Hold it…, Hold the tension…, And then let go…, Relax…, Just relax and notice the changes in the sensations in the muscles of your throat, mouth, and jaw as the tension drains away…, Imagine the tension draining down through your arms and legs and out of your body through your fingers and toes.

…Pause for twenty seconds…

And now notice the sensations in the muscles around your eyes…, What do these muscles feel like?…, Are they tight?…, tense?…, tired?…, or relaxed and smooth?…, Create tension in the muscles around your eyes now by squeezing your eyes tightly shut…, Keep the rest of your body relaxed while you hold the tension in the muscles around your eyes…, What does the tension feel like?…, Hold it…, Hold it…, And relax and let go…, Relax your eyes and notice the changes in the sensations as the tension drains away.

…Pause for twenty seconds…

Now create tension in the muscles around your eyes by again squeezing your eyes tightly shut…, Remember to keep the rest of your body relaxed while you hold the tension in the muscles around your eyes…, What does the tension feel like?…, Hold the tension…, Hold it…, And relax and let go…, Relax your eyes and notice how the sensations around your eyes change as the tension drains away..., At this point, if you have not already closed your eyes you may wish to do so for the rest of the exercise.

...Pause for twenty seconds...

Now notice the sensations in the muscles of your forehead..., What do these muscles feel like?..., Are they tight and tense?..., or relaxed and smooth?..., Create tension in the muscles of your forehead now by pulling your eyebrows down toward the center of your face while keeping the rest of your body relaxed..., Hold the tension in the muscles of your forehead..., Notice the feelings of tension..., What does the tension feel like..., Hold it..., And then relax and let go..., And let your forehead relax and just notice the changes in the sensations as the tension drains away.

...Pause for twenty seconds...

Create tension in the muscles of your forehead again, but this time by raising your eyebrows up as high as you can. Remember to keep the rest of your body relaxed..., Hold the tension..., Pay attention to what the tension in your forehead feels like..., Hold it..., Hold it..., And then relax and let go..., Let go and notice the changes in the sensations as the tension drains away.

...Pause for twenty seconds...

Now, just be still for a minute or so while you scan your body from top to bottom for any areas of remaining tension..., If you notice any such areas, tense and then relax those muscles another time or two or just concentrate on relaxing the muscles without actually tensing them first.

...Pause for thirty seconds...

When you are finished, remain still for a minute or so without opening your eyes..., Notice how you feel..., Make a mental note of what it feels like to have all your muscles deeply relaxed..., What words or images would you use to describe how you feel right now?..., Let those words and images repeat gently over and over like echoes in your mind.

...Pause for one minute...

Now, become aware of your breathing..., Is it deep?..., slow?..., and regular?..., When you are ready, let yourself gradually become aware of the sounds from the world around you..., When you get up from your chair, get up slowly..., Carry the feeling of relaxation with you as you return to the activities of the day..., Whenever you notice that you are feeling tense or stressed, use your memory of the words, images, and physical sensations you have experienced during this exercise to bring back a sense of relaxation and calm.

STRETCHING SCRIPT

Begin to settle down by getting into a comfortable, seated position. Close your eyes and sit quietly for a few seconds while you take several deep..., slow..., regular..., breaths, and begin to become aware of how your body feels.

...Pause for thirty seconds...

Notice your hands..., How do they feel?..., Do they feel tense or loose?..., warm or cool?..., light or heavy?..., Now, slowly and gradually stretch your hands by opening your fingers and stretching them back and apart..., Keep the rest of your body relaxed while you hold a good, comfortable, full stretch in your hands and notice what it feels like..., Hold it..., Hold it..., And now, slowly and gently, relax your hands and let them rest in your lap or at your sides..., Notice the changes in the sensations in your hands as the tension begins to drain away.

...Pause for ten seconds...

Now, do it again. Slowly and gradually stretch your hands by opening your fingers and stretching them back and apart..., Remember to keep the rest of your body relaxed..., Hold a good, comfortable, full stretch in your hands and notice what it feels like..., Hold it..., Hold it..., And now relax your hands and let them rest in your lap or at your sides. For the next several seconds let your hands relax further and further while you pay attention to the sensations associated with your hands relaxing..., Are your hands warmer or cooler?..., Is there a tingling sensation?..., You may wish to imagine the tension draining down through your hands, out of your finger tips, and away from your body.

…Pause for ten seconds…

Good..., Now notice the muscles of your arms..., How do they feel?..., Are they relaxed or tense?..., warm or cool?..., light or heavy?..., Slowly stretch your arms by gradually reaching out straight in front of you. Keep the rest of your body relaxed..., Hold a good, comfortable, full stretch in your arms and notice what it feels like..., Hold it..., Hold it..., And now relax your arms and again let your hands rest in your lap or at your sides..., Notice the changes in the sensations in your arms as the tension drains away.

…Pause for ten seconds…

Now slowly and gradually stretch your arms again by reaching out in front of you..., Remember to keep the rest of your body relaxed..., Hold a good, comfortable, full stretch in your arms and notice what it feels like..., Hold it..., Hold it..., And now relax and again let your hands rest in your lap or at your sides..., Notice the changes in the sensations in your arms as the tension drains away..., Again, you may wish to imagine that the tension is draining down through your arms, your hands, and your fingers, out of your body, and away from you.

…Pause for ten seconds…

Now notice your feet..., How do they feel?..., Tense, or relaxed?..., Slowly and gradually stretch your feet by pulling your toes and feet up toward the sky while you keep your heels resting on the ground...,

Remember to keep the rest of your body relaxed..., Hold a good, comfortable, full stretch in your feet and notice what it feels like..., Hold it..., Hold a good, comfortable stretch..., And now relax your feet and let them rest comfortably on the floor. Notice how the sensations in your feet change as the tension drains away.

...Pause for ten seconds...

Now stretch your feet again by pulling your toes and feet up toward the sky while you keep your heels resting on the ground..., Hold a good, full stretch in your feet and pay attention to what it feels like..., Hold it..., Hold it..., And now relax your feet and let them rest comfortably on the floor. How would you describe the changes in the sensations in your feet as the tension drains away?

...Pause for ten seconds...

Now notice your legs..., How do they feel?..., Slowly and gradually stretch your legs out in front of you..., Keep the rest of your body relaxed..., Hold a good, comfortable, full stretch in your legs and notice what it feels like..., Hold a good, comfortable stretch..., Hold it..., And now relax and let your feet again rest comfortably on the floor.

...Pause for ten seconds...

Stretch your legs out and away from your body again..., Hold a good, comfortable, full stretch in your legs and notice what it feels like..., Hold it..., Hold it..., And relax, and let your feet rest comfortably on the floor. Notice the changes in the sensations in your legs as the tension drains down from your lower legs through your feet, out of your toes, and away from your body.

…Pause for ten seconds…

Good…, Now notice your abdomen and chest…, How do these muscles feel?…, Slowly and gradually stretch your abdomen and chest by sitting back in your chair and arching your abdomen and chest out in front of you…, While keeping the rest of your body relaxed, hold a good, comfortable, full stretch in your abdomen and chest and notice what it feels like…, Hold it…, Hold a good, comfortable, full stretch…, And then relax…, Just let go and notice how the sensations in your abdomen and chest change as the tension drains away. Notice the difference between the sensations of relaxation and tension.

…Pause for ten seconds…

Now slowly and gradually stretch your abdomen and chest again by sitting back in your chair and arching your abdomen and chest out in front of you…, Keep the rest of your body relaxed…, Hold a good, comfortable, full stretch in your abdominal and chest muscles and notice what it feels like…, Hold it…, Hold a good comfortable full stretch…, And then relax…, Just let go…, There is nothing for you to do but to notice the changes in the sensations in your abdomen and chest as the tension drains down and away.

…Pause for ten seconds…

Now notice the sensations in the muscles of your shoulders…, How do those muscles feel?…, Create a full, comfortable stretch in your shoulders now by slowly and gradually reaching out in front of you and then crossing your arms across your chest as if you were giving yourself a big hug…, Keep the rest of your body relaxed while you hold a good, comfortable, full stretch in your shoulders and notice what it feels like…, Hold a good, comfortable, full stretch..., Hold it..., And relax..., Let go and just notice the changes in the sensations in your shoulders as the tension drains away.

...Pause for ten seconds...

Now stretch your shoulders again by slowly and gradually reaching out in front of you and then crossing your arms across your chest as if you were giving yourself a big hug..., Remember to keep the rest of your body relaxed while you hold a good, comfortable, full stretch in your shoulders and notice what it feels like..., Hold it..., Hold it..., And then relax..., Let go and notice the changes in the sensations in your shoulders as the tension drains away.

...Pause for ten seconds...

Very good..., Now notice the sensations in the muscles of your neck..., What do your neck muscles feel like?..., Stretch the muscles of your neck now by letting your head slowly and gently tilt forward towards your chest..., Keep the rest of your body relaxed while you hold a good, comfortable, full stretch in your neck and notice what it feels like..., Hold it..., Hold it..., And relax..., Let go..., Let go, and notice the changes in the sensations in your neck as the tension drains away.

...Pause for ten seconds...

Stretch the muscles of your neck again, but this time by letting your head slowly tilt backward..., Keep the rest of your body relaxed while you stretch your neck. Notice what it feels like..., Hold it..., Hold it..., And let go..., Just let your neck muscles relax..., Let go and notice the changes in the sensations in your neck as the tension drains away.

…Pause for ten seconds…

Now notice the sensations in the muscles of your face…, What do you sense in those muscles?…, Are they tight or relaxed?…, hard or smooth?…, Create a comfortable, complete stretch in those muscles now by widely opening your mouth while lifting your eyebrows…, Keep the rest of your body relaxed while you hold a good, comfortable, full stretch…, Notice what the stretch feels like…, Hold it…, Hold it…, And relax…, Let go…, Relax…, There is nothing for you to do but to quietly notice the changes in the sensations in your face as the tension drains away…, If you have not already closed your eyes you may wish to do so now.

…Pause for ten seconds…

Now slowly and gradually create a comfortable, complete stretch again by widely opening your mouth while lifting your eyebrows…, Keep the rest of your body relaxed while you hold a good, comfortable, full stretch in your face…, Notice what the stretch feels like…, Hold it…, Hold it…, And then let go…, Relax…, Relax…, and notice the changes in the sensations in the muscles of your face as the tension drains away…, Imagine the tension draining down from your face, neck, chest, abdomen, and legs out of your body through your fingers and toes.

…Pause for ten seconds…

Now just be still for a minute or so while you scan your body from top to bottom for any areas of remaining tension…, If you notice any such areas stretch and relax those muscles another time or two, or just concentrate on relaxing the muscles without actually stretching them first…, When you are finished, remain still for a minute or so without opening your eyes…, Notice how you feel…, Make a mental note of what it feels like to have all your muscles deeply relaxed..., What words or images would you use to describe how you feel right now.

...Pause for one minute...

Now begin to become aware of your breathing..., Is it deep?..., slow?..., and regular?..., When you are ready, let yourself gradually stretch and become aware of the sounds from the world around you..., When you begin to move again, move slowly and in a relaxed manner..., Carry the feeling of relaxation with you as you return to the activities of the day..., Whenever you notice that you are feeling tense or stressed, use your memory of the words, images, and physical sensations you have just experienced to rapidly bring back a sense of relaxation and calm.

Autogenic Relaxation Script

Autogenic relaxation is a completely mental relaxation exercise and as such we will begin with a quieting exercise to help build a bit of momentum toward relaxation in the muscles of your body. Do this now by slowly stretching your arms out and above your head and then slowly out to your sides..., Hold a good, comfortable stretch for a few seconds..., and then relax..., Now repeat the same stretch..., Above your head..., and out to your sides..., Hold it..., and relax..., Now, close your eyes and for the next minute do some deep breathing from your abdomen..., Nice slow..., deep..., regular..., comfortable breaths.

...Pause for one minute...

Focus on your hands and fingers..., With each breath that you take think words or images associated with warmth and heaviness in your hands..., Think the phrase: My hands are warm and heavy..., With each breath repeat this phrase or some variation to yourself..., Warm and heavy..., My hands are warm and heavy..., With each breath feelings of warmth and heaviness are flowing into my hands..., With each breath my blood carries feelings of warmth and heaviness to all the muscles of my hands and fingers..., You may wish to imagine that you are somewhere or doing something that would warm your hands such as soaking in a hot tub, lying out in the warm sun, or running warm water over your hands..., Warm and heavy..., My hands are becoming so heavy that it would be difficult to lift

85

them..., Just let these words, phrases, and images of warmth and heaviness repeat like an echo over and over in your mind...,

...Pause for thirty seconds...

Now, with each breath let the feelings of warmth and heaviness flow up from your hands and fingers into your arms..., Focus on your arms..., With each breath that you take think words or images associated with warmth and heaviness in your arms..., Think the phrase: My arms are warm and heavy..., With each breath repeat this phrase or some variation to yourself..., Warm and heavy..., Heavy and warm..., My arms are warm and heavy..., With each breath feelings of warmth and heaviness are flowing into my arms..., Relaxing all the muscles of my arms..., With each breath my blood carries feelings of warmth and heaviness to all the muscles of my arms..., My hands and arms are becoming so heavy that it would be difficult to lift them..., Just let these words, phrases, and images of warmth and heaviness repeat like an echo over and over in your mind.

...Pause for fifteen seconds...

If you get distracted, that's okay. Simply return your attention, gently and easily, to letting the words and images associated with warmth and heaviness repeat over and over in your mind.

...Pause for fifteen seconds...

There is nothing for you to do right now but to enjoy the sense of relaxation that comes with imagining sensations of warmth and heaviness.

...Pause for fifteen seconds...

And now imagine the sensations of warmth and heaviness flowing up from your fingers, hands, and arms into your shoulders, neck, head, and face..., With each breath let the feelings of warmth and heaviness flow up into your shoulders, neck, head, and face..., With each breath that you take think words or images associated with warmth and heaviness in your shoulders, neck, head, and face..., Think the phrase: My shoulders, neck, head, and face are becoming warm and heavy..., With each breath repeat this phrase or some variation to yourself..., Warm and heavy..., So very..., very..., warm and heavy..., My shoulders, neck, head, and face are warm and heavy..., With each breath feelings of warmth and heaviness are flowing into my shoulders, my neck, my head, and my face..., With each breath my blood carries feelings of warmth and heaviness to all the muscles of my shoulders, neck, head, and face..., My eyelids are so heavy and relaxed that it would take a fair amount of effort to open them..., Just let these words, phrases, and images of warmth, heaviness, and relaxation repeat like an echo over and over in your mind.

...Pause for thirty seconds...

And now imagine the sensations of warmth and heaviness flowing down from your fingers..., hands..., arms..., shoulders..., neck, head, and face..., into your chest and back..., With each breath let the feelings of warmth and heaviness flow down into your chest and back..., With each breath that you take think words or images associated with warmth, heaviness, and relaxation in your chest and back..., Think the phrase: My chest and back are warm and heavy..., With each breath repeat this phrase or some variation of your own creation to yourself..., Warm and heavy..., Warm and heavy..., My chest and back are becoming so very warm and heavy..., So very relaxed..., With each breath feelings of warmth and heaviness are flowing into my chest and back..., With each breath my blood carries feelings of warmth and heaviness to all the muscles of my chest and back..., So warm and heavy..., I can feel gravity pulling on my chest and back..., Just let these words, phrases, and images of warmth and heaviness repeat like an echo over and over in your mind...,

...Pause for thirty seconds...

And now imagine the sensations of warmth and heaviness flowing down into your abdomen..., With each breath let the feelings of warmth and heaviness flow down into your abdomen..., With each breath that you take think words or images associated with warmth and heaviness..., Think the phrase: My abdomen is warm and heavy..., With each breath repeat this phrase or some variation to yourself..., Warm and heavy..., Heavy and warm..., My abdomen is becoming so very warm and heavy..., With each breath feelings of warmth and heaviness are flowing into my abdomen..., With each breath my blood carries feelings of warmth and heaviness to all the muscles of my abdomen..., And let these words, phrases, and images of warmth and heaviness repeat like an echo over and over in your mind.

...Pause for thirty seconds...

And now imagine the sensations of warmth and heaviness flowing down into your legs and feet..., With each breath let the feelings of warmth, heaviness, and relaxation flow down into your legs and feet..., With each breath that you take think words or images associated with warmth and heaviness in your legs and feet..., Think the phrase: My legs and feet are warm and heavy..., With each breath repeat this phrase or some variation to yourself..., Warm and heavy..., Heavy and warm..., My legs and feet are becoming so very warm and heavy..., So relaxed..., With each breath feelings of warmth and heaviness are flowing into my legs and feet..., My legs and feet are so warm, so heavy, and so relaxed that it would be difficult for me to lift them…, With each breath my blood carries feelings of warmth and heaviness to all the muscles of my legs and feet…, Just let these words, phrases, and images of warmth and heaviness repeat like an echo over and over in your mind.

…Pause for thirty seconds…

And now, for the next few minutes just let your entire body feel relaxed, comfortable, warm, and heavy…, Focus on the sensations of warmth and heaviness and any other physical sensations or mental images you associate with your present state of relaxation…, With each breath imagine a wave of relaxation washing over your entire body carrying away any tension that may be remaining. Let every muscle of your body become even more warm and relaxed…, For the next few minutes just let the phrases: My entire body is becoming warmer and warmer…, heavier and heavier…, more and more relaxed…, repeat over and over in your mind.

…Pause for two minutes…

Now gradually and easily begin to return your awareness to your surroundings…, Without opening your eyes become aware of the sensations of your surroundings…, When you do open your eyes, just stay where you are for a minute or more…, You may wish to stretch and take a deep breath…, As you return to the activities of the day carry the feelings of relaxation with you…, Every time you notice that you are beginning to feel tense, even a little tense, use your memory to recall the feelings of warmth and heaviness to bring back the relaxation.

SELF-HYPNOSIS SCRIPT

Since self-hypnosis is a completely mental relaxation exercise we will begin with a quieting exercise to help your muscles begin to relax. Do this now by slowly stretching your arms above your head and then slowly out to your sides..., Hold a good, comfortable stretch for a few seconds..., and then relax..., Now repeat the same stretch..., above your head..., and out to your sides..., Hold it..., and relax..., Make sure that you are sitting or laying down in a comfortable position. For the next minute do some deep breathing from your abdomen..., Nice slow..., deep..., regular..., comfortable breaths.

...Pause for one minute...

Continue to take deep, slow, regular breaths while you begin to look passively at an object in the room, a point on the wall or ceiling, or a point on your hand. While you keep your eyes open and focused on whatever you have chosen to look at, continue to take deep, slow, relaxing breaths. Focus with your eyes on whatever you have chosen to focus on and focus with your mind on your breathing. Very soon your eyes will begin to feel heavy but keep them open and focused on whatever you are looking at..., Breath slowly..., smoothly..., gently..., and deeply..., With each breath your eyes become heavier..., and heavier..., Continue breathing and focusing until your eyes feel so heavy that it becomes difficult to keep them open..., When your eyes become so heavy that it is difficult to keep them open, gently let them close while you continue to focus on your breathing..., And as you close your eyes let a special hypnotic word of your own choosing begin to repeat effortlessly in your mind, over and over. It doesn't really matter what word you choose as long as it conveys a sense of relaxation and peace..., It can be any word at all..., You may wish to use a word like "relax," or "letting go," or "deeper," or some other word..., As you let your special trance-inducing word repeat effortlessly like an echo in your mind..., Continue to focus on your breathing and on letting the special word repeat over and over with each breath..., You may be surprised to find that later on you will be able to use your special word to help bring back the comfortable and relaxing state of self-hypnosis that you are even now beginning to experience.

...Pause for one minute...

Continue to focus on your breathing and on repeating your special word..., And begin to let the muscles in your body relax..., And now you can feel your shoulders begin to relax..., All of the muscles in your shoulders begin to smooth out and relax..., And as they relax they begin to feel heavy and limp..., With each breath your shoulder muscles relax more and more..., With each breath you notice how they become more heavy and more limp..., With each breath you feel the increasing pull of gravity on your shoulders as they become more and more relaxed..., With each breath you feel the tension draining out of your shoulders and away from your body..., And notice how these feelings of limpness and heaviness flow very naturally from your shoulders down into your arms and hands so that with each breath your arms and shoulders relax more and more......, And notice how these sensations begin to flow down through your chest and back into your legs and out through your feet..., With each breath..., with each repetition of your special word..., feel the tension draining out from the center of your body through your arms and legs and out of your fingers and toes away from you..., With each breath..., with each repetition of your special word your entire body relaxes more and more..., Twice as relaxed with each breath..., Twice as relaxed with each repetition of your special word..., And now notice how the sensations of warmth..., heaviness..., limpness..., flow up into your face and head so that now with each breath, with each repetition of your special word it is like a heavy warm fluid flowing throughout your body..., Building up..., in the center of your body..., as you inhale..., Draining out through your fingers and toes as you exhale..., Building up in the center of your body as you inhale..., Draining out through your fingers and toes as you exhale..., And with each breath, the flow of the warm, heavy liquid passing through your body relaxes your muscles deeper and deeper..., Deeper and deeper..., And now you find yourself sinking deeper and deeper into the peaceful and relaxing comfort of hypnotic trance..., Imagining that you are walking, almost floating, effortlessly, down..., down a beautiful staircase of twenty five steps, at the bottom of which is an elegantly decorated sitting room with the most comfortable chair you will ever have the pleasure to sit on..., And now, with each breath take a step down the staircase..., And count backward to yourself as you descend the staircase..., twenty-five..., twenty-four..., twenty-three..., and so on..., Sinking..., effortlessly..., deeper..., and deeper..., with each step..., And when you reach the bottom of the staircase you will sit peacefully on the chair while you continue to repeat your special word...,

...Pause for ninety seconds...

And now you begin to look around the room you are seated in..., You begin to explore the room with your eyes..., You may be surprised to find that your chair faces a window looking out on a magnificent view..., or perhaps your chair faces a fireplace where a warm fire burns..., or perhaps you are facing something else..., something relaxing that your unconscious mind has placed in the room for you to look at..., It doesn't really matter what you see, as long as it is comforting..., relaxing..., and completely absorbs your attention.

And you sink deeper..., and deeper..., into your chair with each breath..., Still letting your special word repeat..., over and over..., like an echo in your mind..., And you let your awareness become completely absorbed by the fire, or the view, or by whatever your unconscious mind has provided..., And let yourself sink deeper and deeper..., with each breath..., with each repetition of your special word..., deeper and deeper..., into total relaxation..., And you may discover that it no longer requires any awareness on your part to repeat your special word..., that it repeats automatically with each breath..., and perhaps even in between breaths..., You may not be surprised to discover in the future that you can rapidly return to your present state of deep relaxation simply by controlling your breathing..., repeating your special word..., grasping your left wrist lightly with your right hand..., and imagining this room..., You are so comfortable..., so content..., so relaxed..., that for the next several minutes you will sit peacefully on your chair with your awareness absorbed in the flames of the fire, the view out the window, or whatever it is that you have chosen as the object of your awareness as you become even more deeply relaxed.

...Pause for five minutes...

And when you are ready, it will be time for you to arouse yourself, gently and easily, and return to your normal state of awareness..., In a moment you will begin to count slowly backward from ten to one and as you count you will let yourself become gradually more aware of your surroundings..., And when you have awakened completely you will remain very relaxed, and you will be confident, consciously or unconsciously, that you have the ability to rapidly bring about this same deep state of relaxation whenever you wish..., And now, ten...

...Pause for fifteen seconds...

When you reach the number five let yourself become aware of the sounds of the world around you..., At the number four notice the sensations under your legs and feet and behind your back..., At three you may wish to wiggle your fingers and toes ever so slightly..., Two..., One..., Open your eyes, take a deep breath, and stretch.

MENTAL IMAGERY SCRIPT

Since the use of mental imagery is a purely passive relaxation approach we will begin with a few quieting exercises..., Begin by finding a comfortable position sitting or lying down..., Now slowly and gradually reach out with your arms to your sides or above your head or in front of you and get a full, comfortable stretch..., Imagine that there are strings comfortably attached to the ends of all your fingers which gently are pulling your fingers away from each other and your hands and arms away from your body..., Hold the stretch..., And then slowly and gradually release the stretch..., Now repeat the stretch..., Slowly and gradually..., There is no rush..., Hold it..., Hold it..., And then relax.

Now, focus on your breathing..., Are you breathing from your abdomen or from your chest?..., For the next minute or so deliberately breath from your abdomen..., deep..., slow..., rhythmical breaths..., With each breath let yourself become more and more relaxed.

...Pause for one minute...

Now imagine that it is the early morning of a warm summer day. It is so early that you can barely make out your surroundings..., As you look around you discover that over your left shoulder, behind you, you can see the skyline of a range of mountains outlined in the soft red of sunrise. As you slowly turn and look in the direction directly in front of you, you think you can begin to see the outline of the tops of the mountains on the opposite side of the valley from you. As you continue to look in that

95

direction and as the sun continues to rise the skyline becomes more and more distinct..., As you look down toward the valley floor below all you can see is darkness, although you know that with the passage of just a few minutes you will soon be able to make out some of the details of the valley floor..., But for now, at this magical time of dawn, take a few moments to visually explore what you can and cannot see in your surroundings..., The expanding red of the sunrise and the growing clarity of the details of the mountains behind you..., The emerging skyline directly in front of you..., How the shades of gray melt into inky blackness as you look farther down into the valley and up the valley to your right..., Notice how the darkness of the valley floor merges into the darkness of the sky to your right..., Notice how the red of the sunrise fades to softer red, to pink, to gray, and then to black as you take in the sky above you looking from your left to your right..., Notice how the last stars of night are still visible off in the distance to your right while day is breaking in the distance to your left..., And watch the valley floor as the sun breaks over the mountains to your left..., Notice how it is the valley floor to your right that is first lit by the rays of the sun while to your left the valley remains in the shadows of the mountains..., And watch as the line separating day from night moves, slowly at first, and then more rapidly, from your right, to your left, down the valley floor, until the sun has cleared the mountains to your left entirely, and the whole valley is bathed in the sunlight of morning..., And now look across the valley again to the mountains in front of you..., Notice how the trees of the valley floor carpet the mountains only to a certain height, above which there is only rock and the remnants of last winter's snow..., Observe the contrast in the colors between the grays, blacks, and whites of the rock and snow and the soft blue of the morning sky..., And look down into the valley below where for as far as you can see to your left and right the valley is completely covered in trees..., Every so often looking from right to left along the valley floor you can see the calm blue of a series of mountain lakes..., At times you may suspect that you can see bits and pieces of the river that feeds and connects the lakes..., And look into the sky..., Observe how the blue of the sky changes from a light soft blue near the horizon to a deep clear blue high above you..., Notice how the blue of the lakes below is almost a perfect reflection of the blue sky above you..., Do you see any clouds in the sky?..., A hawk or eagle?..., And now look at your immediate surroundings..., You may be pleased to find that you are sitting comfortably in an alpine meadow high up on the side of a mountain..., Examine the grass and vegetation beneath you and the other objects in the meadow..., Is there a cabin?..., a tent?..., nothing more than a sleeping bag?..., Is there an access road and a vehicle to get you safely home?..., a trail which will lead you home?..., or merely a compass and a map?..., It doesn't really matter what you see in the meadow as long as it is pleasant and relaxing for you..., Take a minute now to continue to visually inspect everything you can see in front of you..., to your left and right..., below you in the valley..., and in your immediate surroundings in the meadow.

...Pause for one minute...

And now begin to notice the physical sensations you can become aware of..., Notice the sensation of the ground under your feet and legs..., the sensation of whatever is supporting your back..., the warmth of the sun on the left side of your face and body and the relative coolness of the last of the pre-dawn air on the right side of your body and face..., Can you feel a light warm breeze from the east?, or a light cool breeze from the north?..., What kind of cloths are you wearing?..., How do they feel against your skin?

...Pause for thirty seconds...

And what can you hear?..., The breeze in the trees?..., the sound of chipmunks, squirrels, or deer in the forest nearby?..., the rush of the air under the wings of a hawk flying overhead?..., the songs of the forest birds?..., the warm crackle of a campfire?..., the sounds of water from a nearby stream or waterfall?

...Pause for thirty seconds...

Can you make out the smell of wood smoke from a nearby campfire or cabin stove?..., the smell of pine from the trees?..., the musty smell of the forest floor?..., the clean crisp smell of the air as the morning dew evaporates?

...Pause for thirty seconds...

For the next several minutes let yourself explore all of these, as well as other, sights, sounds, smells, and physical sensations..., Don't limit yourself to what has been described..., What else comes to you?..., Let your unconscious mind add to and modify the sights, smells, sounds, and physical sensations.

...Pause for five minutes...

If you wish to prolong the sense of relaxation and peace you are currently enjoying you may wish to spend several more minutes imagining how all of these sights, sounds, smells, and physical sensations change over the course of a full day, a season, or a year..., When you are ready, slowly and gradually wiggle your fingers and toes, open your eyes, take a deep breath, and stretch.

Six

Forms

FORMS

"In the long run, nothing can withstand knowledge and experience"
—Freud

The instructions and forms which are described in this chapter will be useful if any of the following situations describe your practice of relaxation:
* You have trouble being organized enough to practice relaxation on a regular basis.
* You are not sure whether you are making any significant progress at learning to relax.
* You wish to be able to demonstrate your efforts and progress at learning relaxation to someone else such as a therapist or physician.

If you want to change something, the first thing you need to do is understand it. Next, you need a plan to make the desired change, as well as a way to assess the effectiveness of your efforts at change. Finally, you need to be ready and willing to fine tune your plan if your original plan does not seem to be working. The forms included in this section are designed to help you with these tasks. Feel free to make copies of the forms as needed.

TRIGGER IDENTIFICATION FORM

Different people are stressed by different things. For this reason it is important for you to learn to recognize your personal triggers for the stress response. To understand how the stress response gets activated in your life it is useful to engage in a bit of self-monitoring. This simply means keeping track, for a week or two, of the situations in which you feel stressed or tense. Stress and tension can result from things you observe or hear about in the world around you, from problems in your relationships with others, and from your own thoughts. The trigger identification form is provided to help you identify your specific stress response triggers. An increased awareness of your personal triggers will make it more likely that your efforts to use relaxation to reduce stress or tension will be successful. Unfortunately, many people learn to relax in the comfort of their home or in a therapist's office but never take the next, and most important step, which is to be able to use the skill of cue controlled relaxation to relax rapidly in the situations in which they are actually having problems.

To use the form most effectively you should take a few minutes each day to reflect on and write down recent events, interactions with others, or thoughts you have had which have triggered your stress response. Write down even minor or mild stressors since these can have a cumulative effect. Once you have identified your most common stress response triggers you can begin to anticipate the situations in which you typically become stressed or tense. Then you can plan ahead to use cue controlled relaxation to help you manage your reaction in those situations.

Trigger Identification Form

Use this form to identify your personal stress triggers. Take a few minutes each day to reflect on the events, interactions, thoughts, and worries that have resulted in feelings of stress, unpleasant physical or emotional symptoms, or problem behaviors for you over the past day and record this information below.

Stress Triggers: Events, Interactions, Thoughts, Worries.

_____

_____

_____

_____

_____

_____

_____

_____

_____

_____

_____

_____

_____

_____

_____

_____

RELAXATION PRACTICE RECORDING FORM

The relaxation practice recording forms are provided for you to use to document your practice of relaxation. There are many benefits to keeping track of the frequency of your practice, the approach to relaxation you have used, and the depth of relaxation you have achieved. Use of this form will help you to be better able to focus your practice in useful directions, to reassure yourself that you are making progress at learning the skill, and to demonstrate the fact that you have been practicing and making progress at developing the skill to your therapist or physician. In addition, if you are having trouble learning the skill the practice recording form will help your therapist assist you in identifying and solving any problems that may be getting in the way of learning relaxation.

Relaxation Practice Recording Form

Use these forms to record your practice of relaxation. Rate your depth of relaxation on a zero to one hundred scale where zero means not relaxed at all and one hundred means completely relaxed.

Date	Number of minutes	Relaxation approach practiced	Depth of relaxation
____	____	____	____
____	____	____	____
____	____	____	____
____	____	____	____
____	____	____	____
____	____	____	____
____	____	____	____
____	____	____	____
____	____	____	____
____	____	____	____
____	____	____	____
____	____	____	____
____	____	____	____

Relaxation Practice Recording Form

Use these forms to record your practice of relaxation. Rate your depth of relaxation on a zero to one hundred scale where zero means not relaxed at all and one hundred means completely relaxed.

Date	Number of minutes	Relaxation approach practiced	Depth of relaxation
___	___	___	___
___	___	___	___
___	___	___	___
___	___	___	___
___	___	___	___
___	___	___	___
___	___	___	___
___	___	___	___
___	___	___	___
___	___	___	___
___	___	___	___
___	___	___	___

Relaxation Practice Recording Form

Use these forms to record your practice of relaxation. Rate your depth of relaxation on a zero to one hundred scale where zero means not relaxed at all and one hundred means completely relaxed.

Date	Number of minutes	Relaxation approach practiced	Depth of relaxation
____	_____	_____	_____
____	_____	_____	_____
____	_____	_____	_____
____	_____	_____	_____
____	_____	_____	_____
____	_____	_____	_____
____	_____	_____	_____
____	_____	_____	_____
____	_____	_____	_____
____	_____	_____	_____
____	_____	_____	_____

Relaxation Practice Recording Form

Use these forms to record your practice of relaxation. Rate your depth of relaxation on a zero to one hundred scale where zero means not relaxed at all and one hundred means completely relaxed.

Date	Number of minutes	Relaxation approach practiced	Depth of relaxation
____	_____	_____	_____
____	_____	_____	_____
____	_____	_____	_____
____	_____	_____	_____
____	_____	_____	_____
____	_____	_____	_____
____	_____	_____	_____
____	_____	_____	_____
____	_____	_____	_____
____	_____	_____	_____
____	_____	_____	_____
____	_____	_____	_____

CUE SHEET

The cue sheet is provided so that you may record the words, phrases, mental images, and physical sensations that you choose to use to help you to bring about the state of relaxation rapidly, even in stressful situations. Once you have developed the ability to attain a state of deep relaxation, pay attention to the words and phrases that you repeat, the mental images you focus on, and the physical sensations you experience while in the deeply relaxed state. After you are finished with your practice, write that information down on the form so that you can memorize it and make use of it to help you relax rapidly in the various stressful situations that invariably will occur in your daily life.

Cue Sheet

Use this form to record words, phrases, mental images, and physical sensations which you associate with being deeply relaxed. You can then use these cues to bring about the state of relaxation rapidly even in stressful situations.

_____

_____

_____

_____

_____

109

PROBLEM LIST

The problem list is provided for you to write down your thoughts about any problems you may be having that are interfering with your ability to achieve deep states of relaxation. If you find that you cannot seem to get relaxed or that you are giving up and not sticking with your practice of relaxation for whatever reason, write down your thoughts about why relaxation is difficult for you. Then review the material in Chapters 2, 3, and 4 to see if the problems you are having are discussed there. If you are working with a therapist, the problem list will help you to let your therapist know the exact nature of the problems you are having so that he or she will be able to help you solve the problems more quickly and easily.

Problem List

Use this form to record any problems you are having with getting deeply relaxed. Read the instructions in Chapters 2, 3, and 4 to see if solutions to the problems you are having are discussed in those chapters. If you are working with a therapist, bring the list to your sessions so that your therapist can help you find solutions to the problems you are having.

Problems I am having with learning to get deeply relaxed:

_____

_____

_____

_____

_____

_____

_____

_____

_____

_____

_____

_____

_____

_____

About the Author

Patrick Davis, Ph.D., is the founder of the Applied Behavioral Concepts Clinic which specializes in the treatment of stress-related physical disorders. In addition to running the practice, Dr. Davis teaches, is an active member of the medical staff at his local hospital, and conducts continuing education workshops for other mental health professionals.